LOOK FOR LADYBUG IN
PLANT CITY

Frances Lincoln
Children's Books

WELCOME TO PLANT CITY

WHERE PLANTS GROW AND LADYBUGS HIDE

Look for the things in CAPITAL LETTERS. Can you find these things in every scene, too?

- Ladybug
- Someone sleeping
- Someone crying
- Five gray mice
- Five bees

LADYBUG GETS LOST

Daisy had a pet ladybug, who was a bit naughty.

One day, Ladybug decided to play hide-and-seek with Daisy without telling her!

Daisy looked around, but she couldn't see Ladybug anywhere.

DETECTIVE BASIL

So she went to see Basil, the best detective in Plant City.

"Please can you help me find my ladybug?" she said.
"Of course!" said Basil. "Tell me all about him."

"Ladybug loves hiding," said Daisy, "but the city is so big and he is so tiny. I am worried that he got lost!"

"What does Ladybug look like?" asked Basil.

"Small and red with black spots and a naughty smile," said Daisy.

Basil wrote everything down in his notebook.

CASE NOTES: LADYBUG LOST IN PLANT CITY
- RED WITH BLACK SPOTS
- NAUGHTY
- GOOD AT HIDING
- COULD BE ANYWHERE

Basil picked up his magnifying glass...

...and gave Daisy a pair of binoculars.

"Let's look for Ladybug!" said Basil.

BIG BONES
PRIMARY SCHOOL

MATH
$1 + 1 = ?$
$1 - 1 = ?$

FRIENDSHIP

TEAM SPIRIT

CONFIDENCE

WE PLAY

WE LEARN

A B C D
E F G
H I J K
L M N O
P Q R
S T U V Z
W X Y Z

READING
HELLO!

STAR
OF THE
WEEK

Daisy and Basil's first stop was Big Bones Primary School.
"Ladybug loves learning," explained Daisy.

They saw an UPSIDE-DOWN RHINO, an ELEPHANT
BLOWING BUBBLES, and a HIPPO EATING ICE CREAM,
but they couldn't find Ladybug. "Let's try the train station," said Basil.

SPORTS

ART

LIBRARY

SCIENCE

THE TRAIN STATION

The train station was very busy. Everyone was rushing to different parts of town. "I wonder if anyone has seen Ladybug?" said Daisy. But no one had time to help them look.

TRAIN DEPARTURES

1 RIVER

2 MUSEUM

3 CITY CENTER

PLEASE DO NOT RUN

TICKETS

INFO

CAFE

GO

MIND THE GAP

BUS 236

BUS STOP

BUS STOP

SCHOOL

They noticed a TAXI FULL OF OWLS, a CAT SELLING
TICKETS, and a RABBIT WAVING FROM A CABLE CAR.
"Let's split up," said Basil. "We'll cover more ground that way."

THE MUSEUM

Basil took a train to the museum. "Maybe Ladybug likes ancient treasures," he thought.

KING

FOSSIL

QUEEN

VASE

ROYAL DOGS

CASTLE

JAR

STATUE

IDOL

DO NOT TOUCH

DINO EGG

VERY OLD CUPS

ODDS & ENDS

Basil explored the museum and discovered
TWELVE MASKED BURGLARS, a PAINTING
OF A PINEAPPLE, and a GREEN SPOON,
but he did not find Ladybug.

SQUIRRELUS & SQUIRRUS
FOUNDERS OF OUR CITY

PLANT

OOKING
ESSELS

EXTINCT
FISH

MAMMOTH
TOOTH

DINO
CLAW

DODO
EYE

LYRE

SEEDS, PIPS,
AND STONES

DINO
POOP

OLD
BONE

ANCIENT TOOLS

ANCIENT
FLUTE

DO NOT
TOUCH

THE FAIR

Daisy visited the fair. "Ladybug loves fast rides," she thought. She climbed up a tree and used her binoculars to look for him.

Daisy spotted a GREEN HIPPO ON A FERRIS WHEEL, a CROCODILE GOING DOWN A SLIDE, and a DOG PUSHING A BUMPER CAR, but she couldn't see Ladybug.

Go!

ENJOY THE RIDE!

HAVE FUN!

THE RESTAURANTS

The two friends met up again for lunch. "Ladybug must be hungry by now," said Daisy.

NOODLE BITES

ROOT PIZZA

PINE CONE CAFE

APHID JUICE BAR

Basil looked closely at all the tasty dishes served at the restaurants. He found a SQUIRREL HOLDING TWO SLICES OF PIZZA, a BIRD FEEDING HER THREE BABIES, and a RABBIT CARRYING SEVEN CUPS but he couldn't see Ladybug anywhere. "Maybe Ladybug wanted to have lunch with his friends at the plant nursery instead," said Daisy.

THE PLANT NURSERY

The manager of the plant nursery showed Daisy around. "This is where all of the plants in the city are grown," he said. "We love looking after them!" Daisy saw a HEDGEHOG WITH A WATERING CAN and a PIG WITH A PITCHFORK, but she couldn't see Ladybug.

WE ♥ TREES

WE ♥ PLANTS

WE ♥ SEEDLINGS

WE ♥ FLOWERS

Basil searched for Ladybug in the greenhouse. He heard a BIRD SINGING A SONG and had a chat with a red-and-black-spotted caterpillar, but no one had seen Ladybug. "Come to the rock concert later," suggested the caterpillar. "Ladybug likes music, doesn't he?"

THE CAVE CONCERT

The rock concert was held in the caves. Lights flashed on and off and everyone was dancing and having fun. Basil and Daisy joined in. "You've got some cool moves!" Daisy yelled to Basil over the music.

The band was called the Screaming Bulbs. They dedicated their coolest songs to a SNAKE WEARING SUNGLASSES, a HEN PLAYING MARACAS, and a FROG IN BOOTS. Basil and Daisy loved the music and dancing so much that they forgot to look for Ladybug.

HEDGE HOSPITAL

QUIET ZONE

MINT TEA

MEDICINES & HERBS

COUGHS

RESTING

HEADACHES

RECEPTION

ER

After the concert, Basil and Daisy walked to Hedge Hospital. Through the windows they saw doctors and nurses caring for the patients.

ITCH CLINIC

BROKEN BONES

They went to the reception desk and asked, "Has a ladybug come in today?" The receptionist checked the patient list. "We've had a SNAKE WITH A BROKEN TAIL, a CHICKEN WITH SPOTS, and a GORILLA WITH A RUNNY NOSE," she replied. "But there's no ladybug on my list."

WAITING ROOM

DENTIST

THE RIVERBANK

"Ladybug loves sailing down the river," said Daisy. "Maybe he hopped onto a boat." She searched down by the water, and Basil climbed into the treetops for a better view.

They met a CYCLING KOALA, a BIRD WITH A BALLOON, and a SWIMMING SNAKE.
But no one had seen Ladybug. "We're running out of places to look!" cried Daisy.
"Not quite," said Basil. "We haven't tried the market yet!"

THE MARKET

"Ladybug MUST be here," said Daisy. "We've looked everywhere else!" She and Basil visited every stall, asking the shopkeepers and customers whether they'd seen Ladybug.

COOL SPECS

FRESH & DRY NOODLES

FLOWERS

FAST WHEELS

PRODUCE

They spotted a CATERPILLAR MUNCHING A LEAF, a WORM INSIDE A ROLLER SKATE, and a SPIDER ON A BALLOON. But Ladybug was nowhere to be seen.

"I miss my pet," said Daisy.
"I'm sorry we still haven't found him," said Basil.
They decided to cheer themselves up by trying on some silly hats.

TEA SETS

SILLY HATS

TRY THEM ON!

BOOKS & COMICS

THE END OF THE SEARCH

"We've looked everywhere and we *still* haven't found your ladybug," sighed Basil.

"Wait," said Daisy. "What's that on your head?"

"My hat," replied Basil.

"It's not your hat," said Daisy. "It's Ladybug!" "He must have switched places when we were in the market!"

"Hooray! We found Ladybug!"

28

"I'm so glad to see you!" said Daisy, giving Ladybug a big hug.
Ladybug smiled his naughty smile.
"Thanks so much for helping me find him, Basil!" Daisy said.
"My pleasure!" said Basil.

"We're a good team, aren't we?" asked Daisy.
"We are!" agreed Basil. "In fact, I've been thinking—would you like to come and work in the Detective Agency with me?"
"Yes, please!" said Daisy, and they celebrated with ice cream.

They were so busy eating that they didn't notice Ladybug sneaking away again...